At the Royal Museum of Scotland

Selected and presented by the Museum Guides
of the National Museums of Scotland

Edited by
Jean Jones and Mary Uhl

NATIONAL MUSEUMS OF SCOTLAND

Published by the
National Museums of Scotland,
Chambers Street,
Edinburgh EH1 1JF

ISBN 0 948636 74 2

British Library Cataloguing in Publication Data
A catalogue record for this book is available from the British Library

Designed by Janet Watson
Printed by Clifford Press Ltd, Coventry, Great Britain

We are grateful to the National Museums of Scotland Charitable Trust
for support for this publication

CONTENTS

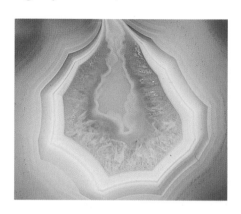

Introduction

The Royal Museum of Scotland brings together an extraordinary variety of material under one roof. Visitors can range through the arts and the sciences, travel the world and travel back in time, without going beyond its doors.

The Museum's collections are drawn from every continent, with displays covering art and design, archaeology and history, animals, rocks and fossils, technology and industry. Fifty exhibits have been selected to provide a sampler of these riches.

They include the rare, the unusual, the mysterious and the entertaining. Some objects are ordinary and everyday, others are remarkable and unexpected. Some are millions of years old, others date from our own century. Between them, they reflect something of the diversity and challenge of life on earth, and of the ingenuity of humankind.

Read about them at leisure, or use this selection to help you explore the Museum's galleries. A free floorplan is available from the Museum's enquiry desk which will help you to locate the galleries, where the featured exhibits are signalled by a ● on the display cases. Each entry is identified where possible by registration number.

If you already know the Museum, this book may take you into areas you have not yet discovered. If this is your first visit, it provides an attractive introduction and guide.

The Museum is active and ever-changing, and it is likely that by the time you read this new galleries will have opened. You can obtain the latest information from the Enquiry Desk in the main hall.

The Museum's Story

The Royal Museum of Scotland was founded in 1854 in response to popular demand for the collection and display of material intended to educate and enlighten. The original Industrial Museum was united with

the University of Edinburgh's Natural History collection in a new building specially designed to house the rapidly expanding collections. Since 1865, when the first part of the building in Edinburgh's Chambers Street opened, there have been several name changes. In 1985 it became the Royal Museum of Scotland.

In the same year the Chambers Street museum, with its international collections, was united with the National Museum of Antiquities of Scotland located in Queen Street. The amalgamated museums and their outstations became the National Museums of Scotland. A new Museum of Scotland is currently being built next to the Royal Museum, to display the Scottish material which decades ago outgrew the available space in Queen Street. The Museum of Scotland will allow visitors to move easily from an exploration of Scotland's past to the international collections which owe so much to Scottish travel and initiative abroad.

The Museum Guides' Story

Under One Roof originated with the work of the Museum Guides. From the first Museum tours pioneered by a handful of volunteer guides in 1991, the Guides' activities have rapidly grown. Backed by a curatorial training programme, the Guides now provide a programme of tours, gallery talks and study sessions to further the appreciation and enjoyment of the collections. They remain a group of dedicated and enthusiastic men and women who give their time, energy and professional skills to the Museum on a voluntary basis.

This book arose from the Guides' work and their first-hand awareness of visitors' interest in the displays. They have chosen fifty objects which illustrate the diversity and quality of the Museum's material, and also reflect their own enthusiasm. The result is a book which is a stimulating guide and introduces the Museum's rich collections.

– 1 –
King and courtier

Limestone relief from Iraq, 9th century BC

King Ashurnasirpal II of Assyria (883-859 BC) presided over the royal palace at Nimrud (biblical Calah) in northern Iraq. He is the figure on the right of this carved stone panel from the North West Palace, the ruins of which were excavated in the 1840s by Henry Layard. The panel is from a continuous frieze.

The king commissioned wall reliefs throughout the palace. They depict him as warrior, hunter, conqueror, worshipper, administrator and overseer of the crops, often attended by officials and divine genies. The reliefs are inscribed with texts, recording with boastful praise the king's considerable military exploits. 'We washed our swords in the sea,' says the inscription about his Mediterranean campaign.

Ashurnasirpal's power and status are clearly evident. His finely carved beard and elaborate hairstyle are striking. He wears a distinctive head-dress, a fringed shawl over an ankle-length tunic, with two knives tucked into the waistband, and in his hand is a bowl for libations. His attendant carries a flywhisk. Both men wear jewellery and carry swords.

The inscription in cuneiform (an early script first executed with reed pens in wet clay) runs across the panel. Over a hundred versions of it have been found in the palace, but this one contains an interesting mistake – three lines have been accidentally repeated.

The relief has been part of Scotland's national collections since 1865, when it was donated by Sir James Young Simpson, an amateur archae-ologist, more famous for discovering the effects of chloroform.

Gallery **G-1** *Main Hall*

Height 2420 mm   A1956.362

– 2 –
Serene perfection
Buddha from Burma, early 19th century

Austere and elegant, this striking figure of the Buddha stands on a lotus flower surmounting an octagonal pedestal. Carved from teak, a tree native to Burma, it was then lacquered and gilded.

The Buddha is represented here in the classical manner with a serene inward-looking expression, large ears, and hair arranged in a stylish topknot. He is dressed in a monastic robe covering both shoulders. The angular treatment of the drapery and the elongated hands add to the impressive effect and are specifically Burmese in style. The position of the hands is not one of the recognized symbolic gestures (or *mudra*) used in Buddhist rituals but the right hand over the heart possibly indicates prayer.

The lotus flower on which the Buddha stands indicates divine birth and sovereignty. It also symbolizes purity and perfection, for the lotus flower grows in mud yet rises immaculate to the surface to bloom. Worshippers bowed down before the Buddha and presented offerings of flowers, incense and flames of light.

Buddhism was introduced into Burma during the 5th century AD and enjoyed the protection of successive Burmese kings. Proclaiming itself as egalitarian and democratic, Buddhism has played a significant part in the movement this century to establish independence from Britain, which was achieved in 1948. It became the official state religion in 1961 and is now practised by 85 per cent of the population.

Gallery G-1 *Main Hall*

Height 2770 mm   A1887.414

ANCIENT COMBAT

Kylix or drinking cup from Greece, about 460 BC

The ancient Greeks were skilled and influential potters, producing a variety of forms for domestic and ritual use. Careful control of the firing process and the use of iron-rich clays resulted in the characteristic black and red colours, used to depict vigorous scenes from history and mythology.

The kylix, a wide, shallow drinking cup, was made using a ceramic technique originating in Greece in around 530 BC. Known as the 'red figure' painting technique, it features red figures against a black ground.

The scene shown here is painted on the centre of the cup's interior. A Greek soldier, on the right with the crested helmet, is in combat with a Persian. Armour, costume and weapons are recorded in detail, highlighting the drama and providing a useful source of evidence for the archaeologist and historian.

The Greeks and the Persians struggled for supremacy in the eastern Mediterranean as the Persian empire made various attempts in the early part of the 5th century BC to annexe the Greek mainland. This scene, like many others on Greek pottery, illustrates the nature of the combat. It complements other battle scenes on the exterior of the kylix, which show mounted archers and foot soldiers.

This piece was given to the Museum by Sir Hugh Hume-Campbell of Marchmont, who acquired a collection of classical antiquities in Italy during the winter of 1843-4. He bequeathed his collection to the Museum in 1887.

Gallery 1-3 *Ceramics*

Diameter of rim 295 mm   A1887.213

Elusive monarch

Slipware dish from England, about 1660

Several elaborate dishes, or chargers, celebrating the restoration of Charles II to the throne have survived. In this entertaining example, the king peers out of the famous oak tree at Boscobel, Shropshire, where he is said to have hidden after his defeat by Cromwell at the Battle of Worcester in 1651. Charles fled back to the Continent, returning as king in 1660 at the invitation of parliament. Here, the oak tree is supported, in the manner of the royal coat of arms, by the lion of England and the unicorn of Scotland.

This type of pottery, slipware, was at the height of its vigour in the late seventeenth and early eighteenth centuries. Most of it was produced in Staffordshire by a small number of potters, including William Taylor who made this dish. Slip is clay and water mixed to a creamy consistency, 'thinner than syrup', according to a contemporaneous account. The thrown or moulded dish was completely covered in slip, dried, and decorated with a thicker, coloured slip, usually black, white or orange.

Using a technique which resembled icing a cake, the slip was squeezed through a tube, often made of wood or cow's horn.

A space in the characteristic trellis border was left for the maker's name. The effect was heightened by adding a jewelling of tiny dots of contrasting colour. Finally, a lead glaze was applied before the pot was fired.

Slipware became less popular when the more sophisticated wares of Wedgwood and other eighteenth-century manufacturers became available, but it has continued to delight collectors. This plate is a rare piece.

Gallery 1-3 *Ceramics*

Diameter 445 mm   A1949.217

Saints in safekeeping

Reliquary from France, early 13th century

In the medieval period relics of saints – fragments of bone, clothing and other items – were powerful symbols. The relics were preserved and cherished, often in beautifully designed and expensive reliquaries.

We do not know which saint is associated with this casket. It is clearly decorated with scenes from the story of the Three Kings. Here on the lid they are following the star of Bethlehem, while on the front panels they are bringing gifts to Jesus and the Virgin Mary.

The reliquary was made in Limoges, in central France, the principal centre of enamel manufacture in the Middle Ages. The Limoges work-shops were organized in production lines with several men working on each piece. This division of labour was necessary to deal with a huge demand generated by a powerful medieval fascination with saints' relics.

The technique of decoration is called *champlevé*. It involved cutting away surface areas from a sheet of metal and filling them with powdered glass in a chosen colour. The sheet was then placed in a kiln hot enough to melt the glass but not the metal. Afterwards the panel was polished and nailed on to a wooden frame. The background of this reliquary has been enamelled in this way, with the figures engraved and then gilded. The heads were made separately and applied to the panel.

Although many of the relics carefully preserved are now regarded as fakes, the reliquaries themselves remain beautifully crafted pieces of work.

Gallery 1-2 *European Art 1200-1800*

Height 218 mm   A1884.44.56

– 6 –
Roasted alive

Maiolica dish from Italy, 1520-30

The story illustrated on this dish tells of an Athenian named Perillus who designed for his master, the tyrant Pharalis, a bronze bull in which to roast his enemies alive. As a reward for his ingenuity, Perillus was the first victim.

The *istoriato* dish (the Italian means 'storytelling') is one of a set commissioned by the Calini family of Brescia to mark the birth of a son. The Calini coat of arms is in the centre of the dish. Each piece in the set illustrates a story from classical Greek and Roman literature, the reading matter of the well-educated. Four other pieces from the set are on display beside it.

Italian noble families traditionally displayed gold and silver as a symbol of wealth and prestige. In the sixteenth century, maiolica, or decorated pottery, became fashionable. Inspired by Renaissance painters, its makers transformed humble earthenware into objects which reflected the artistic developments of the time. The painter of the Calini dishes, Nicola da Urbino, shows his grasp of mathematically exact perspective, contemporary architecture and advances in anatomy.

By the sixteenth century, maiolica was manufactured on a large scale. The pots were dipped in an opaque white glaze containing tin oxide which disguised the brown clay and held the colours in place during firing. The vessels were then painted, often, as here, by a specialist, and fired. The technique, used in Italy from the thirteenth century, was given fresh impetus by later imports of elaborate and beautiful wares from Moorish Spain. These were often shipped via Majorca, which is thought to have given maiolica its name.

Gallery 1-2 *European Art 1200-1800*

Height 270 mm A1897.327

The birth of the Virgin Mary

Carved oak panel, probably from Lübeck,
Germany, 1480-90

Representations of the Christian Holy Family had an important function in an age when many church-goers could not read. Scenes of the birth of Christ are a familiar feature of Christian iconography, but less common are pictures of the birth of his mother.

The infant Mary, her mother, traditionally known as St Anne, and her father Joachim are shown in this vivid family scene. The baby is clearly newly arrived. Anne serenely accepts the offer of food while Joachim, still looking anxious, is congratulated, perhaps by the midwife. The baby is being swaddled by a servant girl. The natural gestures and the warmth and domesticity expressed would have struck chords with the original viewers.

The panel was once part of a larger altarpiece showing scenes from the life of the Virgin, a popular subject in the late medieval period.

There was a constant demand for high-quality religious carvings from the rich Hanseatic trading towns of the Baltic and North Sea coasts. There is an almost identical panel in a complete altarpiece at Vora, in Finland. Both panels were probably made in the Lübeck area. The Woodworkers' Guild there insisted on the use of oak for church pieces, and it is this wood which gives the figures their solid, sturdy quality.

Gallery **1-2** *European Art 1200-1800*

Height 640 mm   A1905.843

Escape from the melting pot

Silver-gilt toilet service from France, mid-17th century

Almost all the magnificent silver belonging to Louis XIV and leading French families was melted down to pay for the king's foreign wars. The Lennoxlove toilet service is one of only three marked Louis XIV services to have escaped this fate. Along with the services now at Chatsworth and Rosenborg Castle, Copenhagen, it was exported before the edicts of 1689 and 1709 demanded the surrender of gold and silver items to the Mint for turning into coin.

The toilet service was found in 1900 in a disused room at Lennoxlove, a tower house near Haddington, East Lothian. It seems to have belonged to Frances Teresa Stuart, Duchess of Richmond and Lennoxlove (1647–1702). A famous beauty, she was described by Pepys as 'the beautifullest creature that I ever saw in my life'. She is remembered today as the model for Britannia on British coins. Frances bequeathed the bulk of her estate to her nephew Walter Stuart, later 6th Lord Blantyre, providing the funds with which Lennoxlove was purchased. The service was probably amongst items from her estate brought from London and installed in the new family seat.

The service was made by two different craftsmen over a period of several years. A specialist candlestick maker, Pierre Masse, made the candlesticks from 1661 to 1663. Recent research suggests that another Parisian goldsmith, Pierre Fourfault, worked on the other pieces. Despite its opulence, it is likely that the Lennoxlove service was a relatively popular design which could be purchased virtually off the shelf.

Gallery **1-2** *European Art 1200-1800*

Height of mirror 555 mm   A1954.8

Pride of lions

Porcelain lion from Germany, early 1730s

The lion was made in the famous porcelain factory at Meissen, founded by Augustus the Strong, King of Poland and Elector of Saxony. The animal is shown at rest, his tail carefully tucked between his hind legs and his forepaws placed demurely together. The impressive mustachioed head has a melancholy, distinctly human, expression.

The lion is probably one of 259 beasts commissioned by Augustus for his new Japanese Palace at Dresden, all intended to be made at Meissen. The palace was designed to house his extensive oriental collection and the finest products of his own factory. A gallery 90 metres (270 feet) long was earmarked for the porcelain menagerie, but production ceased after Augustus's death in 1733, and the gallery was never installed. It is not known exactly how many pieces were completed. A palace inventory of 1735 lists five lions and eight lionesses, and several other large creations survive including an elephant and a rhinoceros. The moulds for these figures were probably made by Gottlieb Kirchner, a leading Meissen artist.

The lion and the other large animals in the series are landmarks in the history of porcelain. Even the Chinese had never attempted figures of this size, as porcelain is an awkward medium on a large scale. A mould was made and clay pressed into it. After firing the mould was removed. Special kilns are required to heat a great mass of clay and sustain its weight. The clay shrinks unevenly and the glaze tends to erase fine detail. Kirchner's finely modelled and elegant lion is a remarkable achievement.

Gallery **1-2** *European Art 1200-1800*

Length 847 mm   A1966.255

– 10 –
Miss Crowford collects

Jewellery and other items, collected in Scotland and abroad, 19th and 20th centuries

M iss Eileen Crowford lived in a small council flat in the Oxgangs area of Edinburgh. From the 1960s onwards she spent her lunch breaks from her work as a typist shopping at local antique shops, pawnbrokers, charity outlets and retail stores. On holiday in Britain, or when travelling to Egypt, India, Ceylon and Russia after her retirement, she continued to acquire ornaments and costume jewellery, and to keep travel tickets, programmes and other ephemera.

Much of this fascinating and varied collection is of inexpensive materials – glass, ceramic, plastic and shell – and in glowing colours. Behind it clearly lies Miss Crowford's own liking for each piece. Nevertheless, she hardly ever wore any of her acquisitions, which were found carefully arranged in drawers and display cabinets, and her friends were not aware that she was a collector. Assembled in this photograph are just a few characteristic items – bird and butterfly brooches, bright necklaces and artificial flowers.

After her death in 1990 it was found that she had bequeathed her collection to the National Museums of Scotland. It was particularly welcome as Miss Crowford had kept a record of the cost and provenance of every item, a valuable document in itself.

The collection, which includes photographs and diaries, is of special value because it offers both a personal insight into the life of an unusual woman and a record of items that in the past have often been considered too ordinary to be worth preserving.

Gallery **1-17** *Modern Jewellery*

Height of largest bird brooch 180 mm

Animals from Ancient Egypt

Hedgehog figurine, 19th-16th century BC,
and toy mouse, 16th-11th century BC

Representations of animals were a common feature in Ancient Egypt. They appear as ritual and decorative objects, and as playthings.

Animal figurines made of faience, the material used for this hedgehog, were popular in the Middle Kingdom period (1900-1500 BC). Faience is made from crushed quartz or sand mixed with lime and natron or plant ash. It is the glaze, derived from copper, which gives it the distinctive blue-green colour. Faience was used for a variety of ornamental objects.

Large numbers of hedgehog figurines have been found in tombs, often as part of a collection of several different animals. The hedgehogs may have been used as amulets, or regarded as symbols of the desert. This one was probably formed round a core of straw. The brown flecks on the back are its quills.

Animal figures with moving parts, dolls, balls, tops, dice and knuckle bones were all favourite Egyptian playthings, and children probably amused themselves with toys of this kind at all periods of Ancient Egyptian history.

The mouse, with its lifelike features, is made from clay or mud, a readily available material, coated with brown pigment chequered with red. The tail and underjaw pivot on pegs on the underside of the body, moving to the jerk of a string. It still has the look of a much-used and much-loved toy.

Gallery **1-20** *Ancient Egypt*

Height of hedgehog 55 mm   A1965.244   Height of mouse 165 mm   A1952.178

– 12 –
IN SEARCH
OF IMMORTALITY

Mummy cartonnage from Thebes, 1000-800 BC

As early as 3000 BC the ancient Egyptians attempted to preserve human bodies after death in order to protect their spirit. Embalming techniques became very sophisticated and refined. First, the organs were removed from the body and preserved. Then the body itself was elaborately bandaged and covered in resin or perfume before being placed in a painted and varnished case.

Cartonnage is made from linen reinforced with resin or, in this instance, plaster. It has been painted with symbols and hieroglyphs telling us that within is the mummy of a priest, Sa, born of Hemsit-Mut.

The symbolism is complex and reflects elaborate beliefs connected with death and the afterlife. The ram-headed bird on the breast wears a sun disc with wings and tail, representing the god Ra. On either side of the tail are the cobra symbols of Egypt, on the left wearing the crown of Upper Egypt, on the right of Lower Egypt. Below is a sekerhawk and figures of Isis and Nephthys, both with green flesh, signifying death, and holding the symbol of life. Their wings protect the deceased. According to legend, the goddess Isis gathered up the dismembered body of her husband Osiris and brought him back to life.

The cartonnage was probably acquired by Alexander Rhind (1833-63), a young Scottish lawyer from Wick who travelled to Egypt for his health. While there, he began excavations at Thebes (Luxor), but in 1863 died on his way home from Egypt. Many of his finds are now in the Museum.

Gallery 1-20 *Ancient Egypt*

Height 1800 mm   A1956.356

– 13 –
Salt sailor

Silver and silver-gilt nef *from Germany, before 1874*

During the late Middle Ages, a model sailing ship was sometimes placed on a dining-table before a king or person of high rank to symbolize his status and power. These ships were known as *nefs*, a word of French derivation. Most seem to have been used to hold eating utensils and napkins, but some were designed to contain salt, bottles of wine and even plates.

This silver *nef* is not medieval, but a comparatively early example of the nineteenth-century German historical revival trend, when earlier styles and designs were imitated. The design of the *nef* is loosely inspired by sixteenth- and seventeenth-century Mannerist work. The maker's mark, an anchor joined with a B, and a pinecone, is the town-mark of Augsburg in Germany, but is not genuine. It was perhaps intended to mislead the purchaser into thinking the *nef* was genuine, or to avoid tax. The maker's mark has not been identified, but is found on a number of interesting pieces of good-quality silver, including two wager cups in the Museum.

About thirty years after this example was made, the firm of Neresheimer & Co in Hanau, near Frankfurt, began to produce large *nefs* on wheels. Many were imported into Britain, and an example is displayed in the same case as the 'anchor B' *nef*.

Nineteenth-century *nefs* were generally made for display on tables or side furniture, although they sometimes have lips at the bow and detachable superstructures which enable a bottle of wine to be placed in the hull.

Gallery 1-5 *Western Decorative Art 1850-2000*

Height 412 mm   A1874.32.7&A

Myth in enamel

Plaque from Edinburgh, 1906

Around the turn of the century the distinctive Arts and Crafts Movement influenced several artists in Scotland. One of these was Phoebe Traquair (1852-1936). Born in Ireland, she studied art in Dublin but came to Scotland at the time of her marriage in 1872 to Ramsay Traquair, Keeper of Natural History at the Edinburgh Museum of Science and Art (an earlier name for the Royal Museum of Scotland).

In the 1880s Phoebe Traquair turned again to the profession she had set aside in order to care for her children. She gained a reputation as enameller, embroiderer, mural painter and illuminator of manuscripts. Her subjects were often allegorical, religious or mythical. The murals for the Catholic Apostolic Church in Edinburgh are perhaps her greatest achievement.

She was attracted by the rich colours of enamelling, and, as well as making small plaques for jewellery, caskets and chalices, executed larger works in this medium. This plaque is one of six which Traquair enamelled to decorate an unusual chalice made from a paua shell. It shows the beautiful Greek princess Psyche abandoned on a remote mountain, a victim of the jealous Aphrodite. A satyr is attempting to comfort, or perhaps to seduce, her. Metal foil heightens the colour, and the figures are outlined in gilt. The chalice itself was designed by Phoebe Traquair's son, also called Ramsay. It is set on a silver and moonstone stand, made by the Edinburgh silversmith J M Talbot.

Gallery 1-5 *Western Decorative Art 1850-2000*

Height of chalice 348 mm   A1989.178

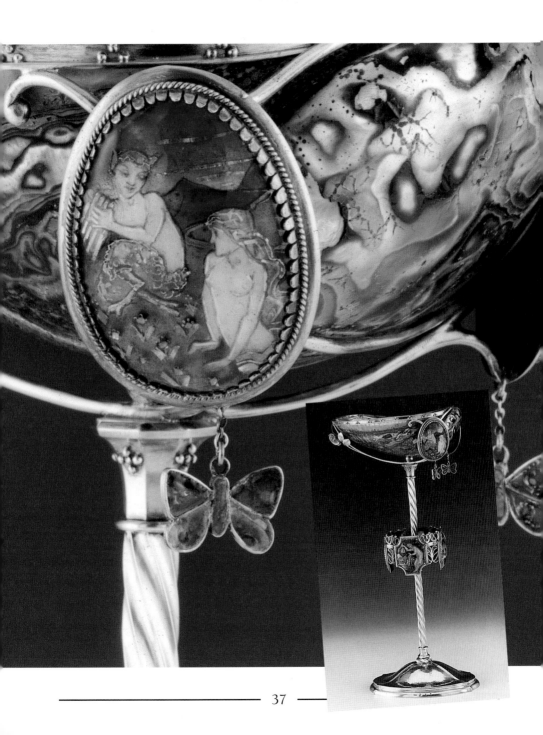

History glass

Glass beakers from Bohemia or Vienna, mid-19th century

The Museum bought these beakers in 1882 believing that they dated from the seventeenth century. In fact, they were probably made in Bohemia or Vienna about 1842 to commemorate the 300th anniversary of Martin Luther's death or to celebrate one of the great nineteenth-century congresses of the Lutheran church. Glassware of this kind, made in the style of an earlier period, is known as *historismus* glass.

A portrait of Luther is featured on one of the glasses, with the dates of his birth (10 November 1483) and death (16 February 1546) inscribed. Above this is the courageous statement he made when called to retract his writings before the famous Diet of Worms, the Emperor Charles V's legislative assembly, in 1521: 'Here I stand, I can do no other.' Also inscribed are the first lines of his hymn, translated by Thomas Carlyle as 'A safe stronghold our God is still, A trusty shield and weapon.'

The book is probably a Bible, which Luther was the first to translate from Latin into German. Its circulation and influence were vastly increased by Gutenberg's recently invented printing press at Mainz.

The second beaker shows Catarina de Bora, a former nun whom Luther married in Wittenberg in 1525. The inscription reads 'Honour God the Father always.' Both beakers show a goose and a sun on the reverse. A goose is the symbol of St Martin of Tours and may refer to the fact that Luther was born on his feast day. Geese are also symbols of marital fidelity, since they pair for life, and this might be another reference here.

Gallery **1-4** *Glass*

Height 178 mm   A1882.31.8 and 9

A Scottish-Spanish alliance

Monart glass from Perth, mid-20th century

Once common and disregarded by connoisseurs, this striking glass is now a collector's item. It was made in Perth where Robert Moncrieff founded the North British Glassworks in 1865. In 1922 the company engaged the services of Salvador Ysart, a Spaniard who had trained in the Baccarat glass-house in France. This followed a well-established tradition, for immigrant workers had been employed in the Scottish glass industry since the seventeenth century.

The company, now known as Moncrieffs, encouraged Ysart to experiment with coloured ware, called 'Monart' glass – 'Mon' from 'Moncrieff' and 'art' from 'Ysart'. Most of the early pieces were vases or bowls but, as demand grew, larger items were produced, notably mushroom-shaped lamps. The rich and varied colours were achieved by rolling hot glass and powdered enamels together and then casing the result in clear glass. This created the deep mottled and swirling colours illustrated here. Often fragments of gold leaf were added to give flecks of gold.

Production ceased during the Second World War but in 1946 Salvador Ysart and three of his sons set up independently in Perth. The new company (named Vasart after Salvador and the initials of his sons Vincent and Augustine) produced the same sort of items as pre-war Monart but in more refined shapes and paler colours.

Gallery 1-4 *Glass*

Height of largest piece 205 mm   MEN 215 (23), LR11/575/55, MEN 215 (22)

BALMORAL ROCK

*Granite contact from Balmoral, Aberdeenshire,
410-650 million years old*

This slab of rock was collected near Balmoral, along the boundary between the granite of the Cairngorms and the deformed and folded strata of the south Grampian mountains, by Professor Matthew Forster Heddle (1828-97) of St Andrews. Later, it was cut and polished in the Museum laboratory.

What does its striking configuration demonstrate? The folded strata below the grey speckled granite are composed of sediments which have been heated and compressed (in geological terminology, 'metamorphosed'). As the granite is not folded the strata must have been deformed before they and the granite came in contact. In some places the granite has pushed its way into the strata. To do this the granite must have been younger than the strata and in a molten state, and molten rock means that the interior of the earth must be hot.

These conclusions may not be surprising today but two hundred years ago they challenged the belief that the earth was cold and that granite and all other crystalline rocks had remained unchanged since the biblical creation. It was an Edinburgh man, Dr James Hutton (1726-97), who proved the contrary by seeking out the contacts between granite mountains and their neighbours, beginning in Glen Tilt just to the south-west of Balmoral. His work helped to lay the foundations of modern geology.

Through applying radiometric methods which make use of the natural radioactivity in rocks, we now know that the metamorphosed sediments are about 650 million years old and the granite about 240 million years younger.

Evolution Wing, **level 7,** *between cases 16 and 17*

Width 717 mm

The anatomy of a boulder

Boulder and pebbles from Auchmithie, Angus,
about 400 million years old

L arge pebbles, cemented together in the course of hundreds of millions of years under the sea, form the fabric of this boulder. The loose pebbles beside it have been broken out of a similar boulder and polished, so that it is easy to see the great variety of material from which it is made.

In the nineteenth century, geologists realized that rough rocks like this, termed 'conglomerates', can provide a great deal of information about the history of a region in distant times. The size of the pebbles suggests that they were derived from high hills which crumbled away in scree slopes and fans. The pebbles are mostly composed of schist and granite, together with quartzite and jasper, revealing the composition of these former hills. Washed down slopes, the pebbles were eventually covered by the sea and cemented with a gritty red sandstone.

The structure of the conglomerate gets steadily finer to the northeast, which suggests that the smaller pebbles were swept along from the south-west – larger pebbles drop out of the current first. To the west, outcrops of schist and granite, stumps of earlier mountains, confirm this supposition. They were part of the Dalradian supergroup formed about 500 million years ago. The conglomerate was formed from their detritus at the beginning of the Old Red Sandstone Period, about 400 million years ago.

Evolution Wing, level 7, *case 43*

Height of boulder 190 mm

Limbless lifestyle

Skeleton of a boa constrictor, Constrictor constrictor, *tropical Central and South America*

The fossil record shows that snakes were the most recent of the reptilian groups to evolve. It is generally believed that the long, limbless body was primarily an adaptation for burrowing, but it also suits other lifestyles: travelling above ground, climbing and swimming.

As in all vertebrates, the skeleton provides the anchor points for the muscles. Snakes generally move by undulations. Strong, segmented blocks of muscles on either side of the body each contract a fraction of a second later than the one in front. As a segment on one side contracts its partner on the other side relaxes, throwing the body into waves which push outwards and backwards. When moving slowly some snakes use a different method of propulsion: they rib-walk. The body remains straight and the ribs move like lots of tiny legs beneath the skin.

The upper and lower jaws are only loosely attached to the wide skull, an unusual but effective arrangement which allows the snake to eat prey much wider than itself. Some snakes have venom, a powerful cocktail of enzymes for digesting their prey, which is injected by means of fangs. Boas and pythons, having evolved neither venom nor fangs, kill their prey by squeezing it until it suffocates. The snake then 'walks' its jaws over its victims in a series of steps made by each half of its mouth separately and alternately. This may take several hours and can leave the snake bloated and immobile for days.

Gallery 2–9 *Skeletons*

Length as mounted 700 mm

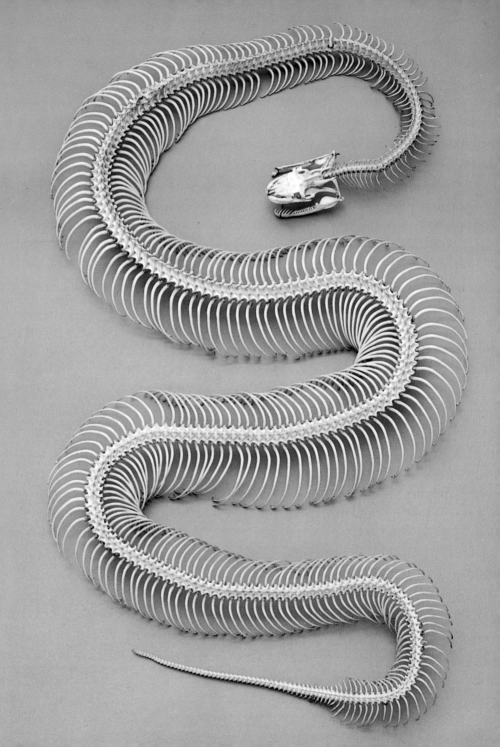

– 20 –
Stone lilies

*Pentacrinites from Lyme Regis, Dorset,
about 200 million years old*

Pentacrinites was a sea creature belonging the crinoid group, whose fossilized members are commonly known as 'stone lilies' and their modern members as 'sea lilies'. This example comes from the limestone cliffs at Lyme Regis, famous for their early fossils, particularly reptiles. They were laid down in the early Jurassic period, that is about 200 million years ago, so these stone lilies are contemporaries of some of the early dinosaurs.

Pentacrinites lived in clumps on the sea floor and is actually an animal though it looks like a plant. Its five segments and flower-like shape are the source of its name, from *pentos* the Greek for five, and crinoid, which means lily-like. The crinoids share this five-fold symmetry with other closely related echinoderms (spiny-skins) like sea urchins and star fish.

The cup-shaped body is situated at the top of a long stem, made up of pentagonal plates of calcium carbonate. The body is protected by an external skeleton of calcium carbonate plates, not always easy to see because of the five large arms whose finely jointed branches swept food into the animal's mouth.

The study of fossils began in earnest in the early nineteenth century when the Englishman William Smith and contemporaries in France demonstrated that different species are found in different parts of a succession of rocks. The relative ages of the rocks can be established through identification of the species interred in them.

Gallery   2–10   *Fossils*

Length 725 mm   G1933.106.1

More than meets the eye

Agate from Usan, Montrose, about 380 million years old

On the outside this rock looks like an old potato. When cut open and polished, a white flame appears to burn in a rosy glow. The overall pattern, a clear chalcedony outer ring lined by sharp bands which circle a colourless crystalline centre, is typical of many agates but they vary enormously in colour and structure.

Agates, composed of chalcedony, a variety of quartz, occur widely, usually in basalt or andesite, two types of volcanic rock. Scotland's numerous volcanic areas are sources of many fine agates. This example comes from the Blue Hole at Usan, south of Montrose, in the nineteenth century the most famous agate locality in the British Isles, but now covered up.

The patterns are formed from layers of crystallized silica gels, trapped in the gas cavities left in cooled volcanic lavas. Generations of mineralogists have been fascinated by the beauty of agates and the processes by which they are formed. These processes are still being studied and researched, at the Museum and elsewhere.

Each agate is unique, which is part of the attraction for collectors and craftworkers, who have used agate to make and decorate many different types of object. Scottish 'pebble jewellery', particularly popular in the nineteenth century, makes use of agate and other types of quartz.

This specimen is one of almost 3000 Scottish agates in the national collection. Two-thirds of these were donated by two dedicated Victorian collectors, Robert Miln and Professor Matthew Forster Heddle.

Gallery 2–7 *Minerals and Gems*

Diameter 60 mm   G210.1908

– 22 –
Urn burial

*Earthenware vessel from northern China,
about 2000 BC*

Pottery was the plastic of the ancient world, versatile and durable. Broken or whole, it can survive for centuries under ground or even under water. This vessel, excavated from tombs at Banshan in the north-western province of Gansu, in China, may be as many as 4000 years old. Excavations show that the people who made this pottery belonged to a late Stone Age culture, known as the Yangshao by archaeologists, which continued into the second millennium BC. Traditionally this period was regarded as the beginning of organized society in China, celebrated with legends of kings and heroes. Archaeology is tending to confirm this claim.

The exact purpose of the vessel is not known but the very fact of its burial in a tomb suggests it was an object of value and significance. The sophisticated curved shape is built up from coils of clay carefully pared to form a narrower base, and the surface is enhanced by a dramatic swirling decoration. All the large vessels from Banshan are of this type, with the decoration ending at the widest part, often in a wavy line.

The red colour comes from iron in the clay. Marks on the surface suggest that the vessel was burnished before firing, probably to enhance the colour. The black and maroon of the decoration were achieved using earths with varying quantities of iron and manganese.

Gallery 2–3 *China*

Height 330 mm   A1929.153

HOME COMFORT

Embroidered hanging from Kerman, Iran

A striking feature of the home in Iran is the use of textiles to drape and furnish the interior. Weaving has been part of the country's culture for millennia, and its characteristic colours and patterns have become known all over the world. Traditionally, the fabrics provided the material and furnishings of the nomad's tent, a protection against wind, cold and sand. Settled communities adapted the tradition to the furnishing of permanent homes.

This richly-coloured hanging was probably used as a curtain or hanging in an urban home. It was made in Kerman, in the central south-east of Iran. The focal point of an area of nomadic groups whose flocks provided the wool for spinning and weaving, Kerman was in the eighteenth and nineteenth centuries a dynamic centre of textile production. It was known particularly for its production of knotted wool carpets, and shawl fabric for both furnishing and clothing.

The plain fabric has been embroidered with coloured wools, in flat filling stitches which imitate the effect of a woven material and provide a substantial texture. Highly-skilled embroidery was an important aspect of Kerman's textile industry. While the weavers were men working in special premises, the embroiderers were women, working in the home.

The design itself is a characteristic blend of traditional cone, medallion and floral patterns, which have become well known in Europe, particularly through the popularity in the nineteenth century of the Paisley shawl. The strong but subtle colour and the spirited interpretation ensure that this hanging would add warmth and distinction to any home.

Gallery 2–12 ***Within the Middle East***

Length 2600 mm   A1921.1415

– 24 –
Imperial style

Dragon robe from China, 18th century

Dragon robes were worn on ceremonial occasions by the emperors of the Qing dynasty (1644-1911) and their family and officials. The imperial family were Manchus, originally a northern nomadic tribe, and the style of the dragon robes, with their cross-over fronts and wide sleeves, is derived from traditional Manchu garments which allowed ease of movement on horseback.

Dragons first appeared as a motif on clothes a thousand years earlier, during the Tang dynasty (AD 618-906), and gradually evolved into the characteristic decoration of dragons and Buddhist symbols seen on this robe. To the Chinese, dragons were benevolent, adaptable creatures, symbolic of many attributes including imperial power.

The colour and decoration of the robes were assigned according to rank. In 1760 regulations were issued restricting the use of yellow silk to the emperor and his immediate family. The nine dragons and brown silk of this robe suggest a senior member of the court. Birds, clouds, waves, flames and medallions appear above a deep band of diagonal stripes.

The embroidery is executed in brilliantly dyed silks and gold thread. Several different stitches are employed, including satin and stem stitch, Peking knots, and a technique known as couching whereby the thread is laid on the surface and secured by tiny stitches. The gold thread itself was made by wrapping strips of gold leaf round silk.

With the fall of the Qing dynasty dragon robes largely disappeared except in traditional Chinese theatre and as tourist and export commodities.

Gallery 2–2 *Ivy Wu Gallery*

Length 1310 m m   A1967.415

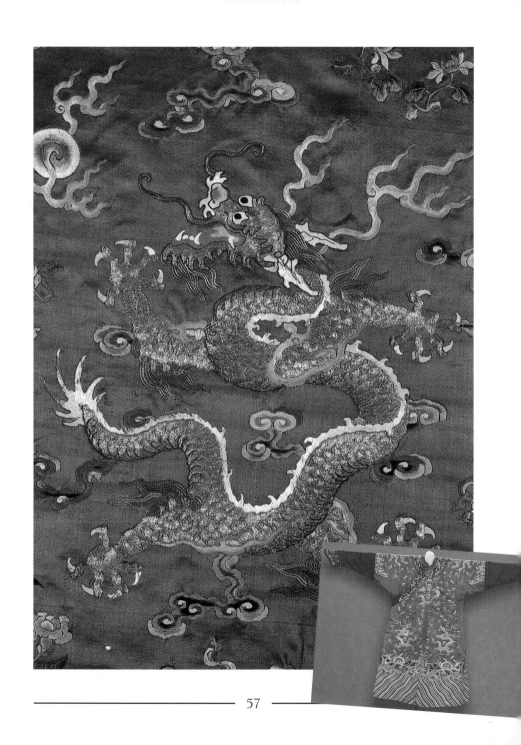

25

East Indiaman

Model of the D'Bataviase Euew, *Holland, 1719*

'East Indiaman' is the term used to describe the ships belonging to the Dutch East India company, founded in 1602. With trading posts and factories from Japan to Iran, the Company dominated trade with the Far East for nearly two hundred years, supplying new and exotic goods, such as porcelain, tea, silk and spices, to eager customers in Europe.

This model of the *D'Bataviase Eeuw* (The Batavian Century) has the name and date (1719) carved on the richly decorated and gilded stern. However, Company registers do not record a real ship of this name, and the model may have been commissioned, perhaps for the Company's head-quarters in Amsterdam, to commemorate the centenary of the founding of Batavia (in Indonesia, now Jakarta) as its eastern centre of operations.

The model was built in the same way as a real ship, and is a valuable record of Dutch ship construction. The hull is original apart from some minor restoration, but the rigging and sails were replaced in the 1930s. The lateen (triangular) sail on the mizzen (rear) mast is typical of many ships of the period.

The scale of the model is about 1:28. Ships of the time were some 50 metres (170 feet) overall, with a mainmast rising 40 metres (130 feet) from the deck. They carried guns to protect their valuable cargoes from pirates and nations with which Holland was formally at war.

At the height of its power the Dutch East India Company owned about 190 ships. Its monopoly of European trade in East Asia was successfully challenged by the British and French and the Company was dissolved in 1798.

Gallery 2–2 *Ivy Wu Gallery*

Length 1930 mm   T1882.28.18

26

Fiery cockerels

Incense burners from China, 18th/19th century

The cockerels are incense burners, with wings that open to allow a layer of heat-absorbing sand to be poured inside. When ground-up sandalwood mixed with spices is sprinkled on top of the sand and set alight, fragrant smoke curls from beneath the wings. Incense has many functions in China and is still burned in temples and in homes where its traditional use is to expel insects before windows are closed for the night.

The cockerels were enamelled by the *cloisonné* technique, introduced into China from Europe in the fourteenth century. Fine metal wires were soldered onto the copper alloy base to form little cells or *cloisons*, which were filled with coloured glass pastes and then fired. After cooling, the surface was polished smooth and the metal parts gilded.

At first the Chinese regarded enamelling as vulgar but in time, adapted to Chinese taste, its decorative possibilities were exploited to the full by the imperial workshops. After the looting of the Summer Palace outside Beijing in 1860 by French and British troops, many magnificent *cloisonné* pieces came to the attention of European collectors who then began to seek out other examples.

The fiery cockerel is much admired by the Chinese. Anyone born in the Year of the Cockerel (1933, 1945, 1957, 1969, 1981 and 1993) is said to inherit its courageous spirit.

Gallery 2–3 *China*

Height 198 mm   A1980.63 & 64

27

Celestial dancer

Sculpture of a surasundari from northern India,
11th century

A great school of architecture and sculpture flourished in northern India under the Chandella dynasty of the tenth and eleventh centuries. This graceful figure comes from the famous complex of temples at Khajuraho, about 250 kilometres (150 miles) west of Allahabad.

The human figure played an important part in Hindu art, much of which draws inspiration from the personalities and actions of gods and goddesses. The feminine principle is manifested in many forms, generically known as Devi. Some are well defined, such as the blood-thirsty goddess Kali. Others, like the surasundaris, have a less specific identity. As celestial nymphs, they have an idealized femininity and are often shown as dancers. There were large numbers of surasundari sculptures at Khajuraho.

Carved in fine-grained red sandstone, this example stands in the classic Indian *tribhanga* pose – the weight on the right foot with the hip pushed out and curving to the left, the head and neck erect. Even though the figure is broken off below the hip and has lost a hand, the effect is still one of great fluidity.

The lines of her body are accentuated by her clothing and her jewellery, which also highlight a sense of movement. She wears a stole across her shoulders and a loin cloth, or lungi, and an elaborate necklace and belt. Her conical headdress, the *karanda-mukata*, is decorated with five lotus buds.

Gallery 2–3 *China*

Height 1180 mm   A1971.704

28

WATERPROOF

Cape made of seal intestines, from the Aleutian Islands, Alaska, mid-19th century

Keeping dry was important for the Aleut people, as much of their life was spent on water. Marine mammals were the traditional source of their clothing.

Aleut women were skilled craftswomen who made garments such as this cape from strips of seal intestines sewn together with gut thread. The thread swells when it gets wet, closing the holes through which it passes and making the clothes completely waterproof.

This particular cape probably had a ceremonial use. *Parkas* (a garment we have copied from the Aleut and the Inuit) were worn for hunting and fishing, as well as on other occasions, and were not decorated to this degree. The overall design with its flowing body, wide sleeves, and high neckline shows strong Russian influence: the Russians were the first Europeans to settle in Alaska.

Though the shape of the garment is Russian, the decorative borders with their linear and zigzag patterns are Aleutian, and are similar to those on some of their artefacts. The borders are made from strips of dyed sealskin sewn with a zigzag stitch. Feathers decorate the neck, and tiny tufts of European wool are sewn into some of the seams. Traditionally the Aleut women pushed the thread through holes made with an awl but this cape was probably made using European steel needles.

Alaska was bought from the Russians by the USA in 1867. As mining and large-scale fishing intensified the disruption to the Aleut way of life these ceremonial garments ceased to be made.

Gallery   2–20   *Tribal Art*

Length 1180 mm   A1869.30

– 29 –
Appeasing the spirits
Helmet mask from New Ireland, late 19th century

New Ireland lies about 600 kilometres (400 miles) east of New Guinea. Invaded by Europeans and later by the Japanese, it became part of independent Papua New Guinea in 1975.

Although many New Ireland traditions no longer survive, the important funeral ceremonies held every four or five years, known as Malagan, still persist in certain villages. The spirits of the dead, thought to remain among the living, are celebrated or appeased. This mask was probably worn during the Tatanua, a sacred dance which is part of Malagan.

The mask is made of wood, painted in traditional colours. White, produced from crushed coral and lime, is an adjunct to magic spells. Black, the pigment from a local nut, is associated with warfare, while red, made from crushed rock, recalls spirits who have died through violence. The hair, fixed to a cane and fibre headpiece, is made from dried tree fibres, and imitates the people's traditional method of dressing their hair during mourning. The eyes are made from snail shells. The meaning of the painted wooden leg can only be guessed at.

New Ireland artists are small in number and are held in high esteem. Carvings for Malagan are specially commissioned by village communities and in the past were deliberately left to perish after use.

Gallery 2–20 *Tribal Art*

Height 665 mm   A1890.58

30

Hornblower

*Ceremonial figure from Benin, south-west Nigeria,
17th or 18th century*

The brass hornblower from Benin is rare and striking. Representing a palace musician playing an ivory side-blown horn, the figure wears a collar of leopard's teeth and the tie of his wrapper is decorated with a leopard mask. The leopard symbolized kingship and leopard ornaments were worn only by the *oba*, or king, and chiefs of high rank. Such a figure stood alongside others within the palace courtyard on altars dedicated to the *oba*'s ancestors.

The brass-casters of Benin City lived as part of the royal household, with their own place in the hierarchy, and were responsible solely to the *oba*. They used the lost wax technique of casting, whereby wax is placed round a clay core, which has been modelled to the desired shape. This is covered with more clay and then fired. After the wax has melted, the space it occupied is filled with molten metal. When the metal has hardened, the clay is broken away. The lost wax technique allowed for extremely intricate detailing. The copper alloy of this figure is brass (copper with zinc) although Benin smiths at earlier periods did use bronze (copper with tin).

Benin metalwork was one of the first African art forms to excite European interest, beginning in the late 1890s. It was so sophisticated that at first it was thought that Africans must have learned the technique from Europeans. Today, however, the art of Benin is fully recognized not only as indigenous but as a landmark in African and world art history.

Gallery   2–20   *Tribal Art*

Height 645 mm   A1985.630

31

Turkish delight

Earthenware dish from Iznik, Turkey, late 16th or early 17th century

The painting on this shallow dish, with its graceful design springing from the rim, is typical of pottery made in Iznik (the ancient city of Nicea), some 130 kilometres (80 miles) east of Istanbul.

Iznik was renowned for pottery with strikingly graceful floral designs in bold colours. The tulips and carnations on this dish are characteristic of its distinctive decoration. The dish is made of a white clay and quartz paste with the design painted under a colourless glaze. The strong colours are derived from cobalt blue, from Iran, and a local orange-red clay. Cobalt was important in ceramic history as it sparked off the manufacture of Chinese blue-and-white porcelain, which was imported into Europe where it influenced local styles. Iznik wares were to adopt Chinese motifs such as the stylized rock and wave pattern seen round the rim of this dish.

Turkey was the centre of the Ottoman Empire, which extended from Central Europe to the Middle East. Trade links stretched contact even further, and there were many mutual influences and exchanges. Turkish pottery, like carpets and textiles, became known in Europe.

The finest wares were made in the sixteenth and seventeenth centuries, which saw the production of large quantities of tableware and thousands of tiles used in the decoration of mosques, public buildings and private homes. The Iznik potteries declined in the seventeenth century but their distinctive products still embody the vibrancy of Ottoman art.

Gallery **2–4** *World of Islam*

Diameter 335 mm   A1883.18.3

32

The fish and the waterfall

Iron sword guard from Japan, late 19th century

Samurai swords, belonging to Japan's hereditary military class, were the best cutting weapons in the world, essentially unchanged for a thousand years. However, their function became largely ornamental after internal samurai warfare ceased and Japan was unified in the seventeenth century.

The sword guard, or *tsuba*, shaped to match the top of the scabbard, protects the hand by separating the hilt from the blade. The central opening takes the blade, while the two smaller openings fit over the hilts of two knives, also kept in the scabbard. Sword guards were just one element in the sets of sword fittings, at their most elaborate in the late Edo period (1750-1868), which demonstrated the status and taste of their owners.

Within the strictly defined limits of this small surface area the crafts-men could show off their ingenuity in metalworking and choice of subject. Japanese and Chinese legends and history provided a rich source of inspiration, as did the natural world.

This *tsuba* is made of iron and highlighted with gold. The gilded carp struggling to leap up a waterfall represents the persistence needed for success. On Boy's Day (3 March) any house with a son under eight still displays a streamer in the shape of a carp, signifying a wish for perseverance throughout the boy's life.

When Japan modernized her army in the late nineteenth century the treasured weapons of the samurai became curiosities almost overnight, and many *tsuba* found their way into Western collections to be valued as art in miniature.

Gallery 2–4 *Japan*

Length 740 mm   A1895.167

– 33 –
East meets West

Enamelled porcelain bowl from Japan, late 17th century

The first Europeans to establish trading contact with Japan were the Portuguese in the early sixteenth century. But relations broke down and from 1600 until 1868 foreigners were banned from Japan. When Europe's trading connections with China were disrupted by civil war between 1657 and 1682, Dutch merchants turned to the Japanese. They were allowed to trade, but were restricted to an island in Nagasaki harbour.

The Dutch at first commissioned local craftsmen to imitate the blue-and-white porcelain no longer obtainable from the Chinese. Then the eyecatching native enamelwares attracted their attention. The technique of enamelling involved painting previously glazed and fired vessels with a rich variety of enamel colours before refiring them at lower temperatures.

The painter of this dish has combined design features long popular in Japan with aspects arising from a foreign presence. He may never have actually seen a foreigner, and may have had to work from a drawing. He has reproduced the Dutchmen's fashions accurately (note the high heels) but evidently chose the colours himself. While the traders all have fair hair as a mark of their foreignness, their jackets are decorated with Japanese patterns. The flags flying from the ships should have been red, white and blue. In Japan the possession of firearms was an offence punishable by death, so the painter may have found the firing cannon as exotic as the Dutchmen's appearance.

The whole effect, with its crowded scenes and bright colours, is an early example of aspects of Western gaudy taste which influenced some Japanese designs.

Gallery 2–4 *Japan*

Diameter 83 mm   A1947.132

34

Records from the tomb

Earthenware horse from Japan, 7th century

The horse comes from a burial mound at Osatu, near Tokyo. New techniques of farming and metalworking were introduced into Japan in the early years of the first millennium, and a warrior aristocracy was established. The most important members of this ruling class were buried in multi-chambered stone tombs covered with huge mounds of earth. Many of these are found near Tokyo where the tombs were first developed in the sixth century.

Pottery cylinders, known as *haniwa* in Japanese, were placed in the earth round the mounds, probably to prevent the earth from slipping. Originally plain, they were later shaped at the top into representations of objects which had been of significance to the deceased, especially houses, people and animals. Horses were one of a warrior's most prized possessions.

The information *haniwa* give us about life in Japan at this remote period, for which there are few written or painted records, make them of particular interest. Features such as the details of the horse's harness are valuable evidence.

The construction is quite elaborate. The horse's legs and initially the body were made from cylinders built up from coils of clay smoothed on the outside. This ancient technique was useful as it employed less clay than a solid body would have done, and a great number of *haniwa* were needed for each mound. Hollow cylinders were less likely than solid clay to crack during firing, and were the most practical shape for sinking into loose earth.

Gallery 2–4 *Japan*

Height 554 mm   A1910.73.6

35

IN TRIPLICATE

Teaching microscope from France, 1860

Those of us who find it difficult to identify anything under a microscope, or are deluded into thinking that our own eyelashes are some strange new creature, will instantly see the advantages of this instrument. Known as the 'triple demonstration microscope', it allows a teacher and two students to examine a specimen on a slide simultaneously. Each viewer is able to operate the microscope independently, as each eyepiece tube has its own adjustable focus.

The microscope was made by a famous and innovative Parisian firm, Nachet et Fils. It was bought for the Physiology Department of the University of Edinburgh during the professorship of John Hughes Bennett (1812-75). Bennett, who is best known for his discovery of diseases of the blood including what was later known as leukaemia, had trained in France and Germany where microscopy was an integral part of the medical course. He quickly recognized its importance in the clinical investigation of disease, and was aware that the development of bacteriology and embryology required new instruments for the practical side of diagnosis.

Before Bennett was appointed to the chair at Edinburgh he became one of the first teachers in Britain to insist that his students learn to use microscopes systematically. This had a profound effect on medical education. This microscope played a part in his reforms. It is one of a range of microscopes used in many different branches of science, which are displayed in the Instruments of Science gallery.

Gallery   **2–18**   *Instruments of Science*

Height 300 mm   T1980.L9.11

36

Calculating the calendar

Astrolabe from Moorish Spain, 11th century

Astrolabes are complex scientific instruments which played a vital role in the leading medieval science, astronomy. Their primary use was in undertaking calculations. Because calendrical computations were also performed with them, they could be employed to assist in casting horoscopes. They could be used to measure the altitude of the sun and of stars, and from these observations compute the time (modern experiments have shown that they were accurate to within ten minutes).

Originally invented by the Greeks, astrolabes were perfected by Islamic scholars at a time when scientific enquiry had virtually ceased in the West. Greek and Arab science eventually made its way into Europe through contacts between scholars from Europe and Moorish Spain. This particular instrument was made in Toledo nearly a thousand years ago by a craftsman called Muhammad bin as-Saffar. It is extremely rare and precious, the oldest known signed and dated astrolabe made in Europe and a symbol of the revival of science in the West.

After being widely used for many centuries, astrolabes were gradually replaced by other instruments, but even today traditionalists in Islam sometimes employ them to perform calendrical calculations.

Astrolabes have always been treasured as symbols of learning and as exceptional examples of the metalworker's art.

Gallery **2–18** *Instruments of Science*

Diameter 210 mm   T1959.62

37

Electric currents

Current balance from Glasgow, about 1895

This handsome brass and copper instrument, which measures currents and voltages, was designed by William Thomson, Lord Kelvin (1824-1907), Professor of Natural Philosophy at the University of Glasgow from 1846 to 1899. Kelvin made notable contributions to the theories of heat, electromagnetism and geomagnetism, and pioneered many practical applications of his discoveries. He was the first scientist to be given a peerage for his public services.

Two of the fast developing technologies of the day were telegraphy and electric lighting. Since electricity had to be measured before it could be used safely and effectively, Kelvin designed and improved a great range of measuring instruments for electrical engineers. He also campaigned for electrical standards.

Kelvin's designs, manufactured under patent, earned him a fortune. Many of them were made by a Glasgow colleague, James White, who became one of the foremost instrument makers in the country. The business carried on after White's death in 1884, with Kelvin coming in as a partner, and it was at White's that this particular current balance was made.

It was Kelvin's work on the transatlantic telegraph cable, one of the most heroic technical achievements of the Victorian era, which first brought him fame. Convinced that a cable this length was feasible, he designed instruments which could pick up very faint signals. He oversaw the manufacture of the cable, and provided encouragement when the first attempts to lay it failed. It eventually came into operation in 1866. Fragments of the first, unsuccessful, cable are on display near the current balance.

Gallery **2–18** *Instruments of Science*

Height 190 mm   T1902.30

38

Pocket calculator

Napier's rods or 'bones', from Scotland, early 17th century

This basic calculating aid works by substituting the simpler process of addition for multiplication. The faces of the rods are marked out with the multiplication tables of the digits from one to nine. Users did not need to know their tables, only how to manipulate the rods and how to add and subtract.

The rods were designed in the early seventeenth century by John Napier, Laird of Merchiston (1550-1617). They were intended to make multiplication, division and the calculation of square and cube roots less difficult for beginners.

As the inventor of logarithms Napier achieved instant European-wide recognition for having provided a powerful new computational tool for mathematicians. There is now a university named after him, which incorporates the remnants of his home, Merchiston Castle, now in the suburbs of Edinburgh.

The popular name of 'bones' for the calculating rods may reflect the fact that Napier died a few months before his book about them was published; or the name may derive from the ivory or bone used to make early sets. This set is made of ivory.

In his own day Napier was known to his countrymen as a strong supporter of the Scottish reformation, an author of trenchant Protestant tracts. Two centuries later, Sir Walter Scott had one of his characters swear 'by the bones of the immortal Napier', so raising a long forgotten calculating device to that of a saintly relic! Only informed nineteenth-century antiquaries would have recognized the pun.

Gallery 2–18 *Instruments of Science*

Length 60 mm   NL 43

39

Charismatic chemist

Glass apparatus from Edinburgh, Scotland,
late 18th century

Joseph Black (1728-99) was an active figure in the intellectual movement now known as the 'Scottish Enlightenment'. Investigating the chemistry of lime water for his Edinburgh MD thesis (1754) he discovered a 'fixed air' with distinctive chemical properties – the gas carbon dioxide. At the University of Glasgow he found that heat was needed to change a solid into a liquid, or a liquid into a gas – latent heat. Both these advances had far-reaching effects for the development of chemistry and physics.

By the time Black was appointed Professor of Chemistry at the University of Edinburgh in 1766, he was internationally famous. His reputation drew students to Edinburgh from as far afield as America and Russia. From surviving students' lecture notes we know the content of his lectures. His students were struck by his dexterity when conducting experiments: he 'could pour boiling acid from a flask without a neck and never spill a drop'.

The clear glass bottle still contains calcium carbonate and may have been used to generate carbon dioxide. The green vessels are a cucurbit and alembic, and a curved retort. The vessels, probably made in a bottle factory in Leith, were used for distillation. This sturdy apparatus was employed in the demonstrations with which Black illustrated his lectures.

Black's successor took over the class collection of apparatus. In 1858 a subsequent Professor of Chemistry recognized that objects relegated to a lumber room were priceless relics of one of the founders of modern chemistry. He presented the surviving pieces to the Museum. Chemists from all over the world still come to see them.

Gallery **2–18** *Instruments of Science*

Height of retort 350 mm   T1858.275.36 (centre), 38 (left) and 40

40

Building the Forth Bridge

Theodolite from York, England

A famous Scottish engineering firm, Messrs Tancred Arrol and Company, commissioned this surveying instrument, known as a theodolite, when they were involved in building the Forth Railway Bridge.

Extensive surveying was necessary before and during construction of this massive triple-cantilever bridge, 2552 metres (8295 feet) long, to ensure that the structural components were exactly aligned. The theodolite was specially designed by Thomas Cooke and Sons, a York firm internationally famous for its precision instruments.

Possibly the most important surveying instrument ever invented, the theodolite measures the angles between distant points and the horizontal or vertical. The position of a distant point can be calculated by trigonometry, a discovery made by Greek astronomers around 160 BC. This method, known as triangulation, has long been used in surveying, map making and building construction.

The construction of the Forth Bridge was the nineteenth century's most ambitious civil engineering project in Scotland. It relied for its success on state-of-the-art instruments and technology. This instrument is more complex and sophisticated than the basic theodolite, as it had to deal with great heights at a short distance.

The bridge has become a symbol of nineteenth-century achievement. Crossing the Forth a century on, we can appreciate its magnificence, while instruments such as the theodolite give us some understanding of what a massive technological achievement the bridge represents.

Gallery **2–18** *Instruments of Science*

Height 410 mm   T1987.111

41

SAFETY AT SEA

Fresnel lens from France, 1826

In the first half of the nineteenth century great efforts were made to design lighthouse optics that would project a brighter light than the silvered reflectors of the time.

This lens was made by the Parisian optician, François Soleil, to the design of Augustin Fresnel, a physicist and Secretary to the French Lighthouse Commission. Of a type known as a 'Fresnel lens', it is composed of ring-shaped prisms around a central lens, and could be made much larger than a conventional lens. Several, rotating round a light source, were used to project powerful beams from lighthouses.

In Britain for much of the nineteenth and early twentieth centuries the Engineers to the Northern Lighthouse Board, responsible for Scotland and the Isle of Man, were members of the Stevenson family of civil engineers who came to lead the world in lighthouse technology. (Robert Louis Stevenson was from the same family.)

The Stevensons were quick to adopt the lenses developed by Fresnel. In 1824 Robert Stevenson visited him in France to study his work. He ordered lenses to assess for the commissioners of the three British Lighthouse Boards. The first British use of Fresnel lenses in a lighthouse was in 1835 at Inchkeith in the Firth of Forth. In time they were adopted in all large lighthouses.

The Museum's lens was purchased from Soleil in 1826 by Sir John Leslie, Professor of Natural Philosophy at the University of Edinburgh. It forms part of an important collection of teaching equipment donated to the Museum in 1975.

Gallery   **2–18**   ***Instruments of Science***

Diameter 830 mm   T.NPM.C2

42

The practice of power

Helm from Herefordshire, England, before 1375

Formerly this helm hung over the tomb of Sir Richard Pembridge (died 1375) in Hereford Cathedral, a symbol of his authority and a reminder of his military distinction. Constructed from three plates of steel riveted together, the helm was designed to deflect attack. A low crown plate is overlapped by a sloping plate shaped like a truncated cone, in turn overlapped by a vertical plate made all in one piece. The raised edges of the eye hole give extra protection. Chains with toggle ends were passed through the cross-shaped holes to attach the helm to the breastplate.

The helm was originally lined with leather or cloth and worn over a cloth cap and a mail hood. Internal padding, secured between the holes in the sides, ensured a snug fit. Sir Richard's identifying crest, a wheat-sheaf, was attached through holes at the top. The style of the helm is both effective in defence and deliberately sinister, to intimidate opponents.

Sir Richard came from a Herefordshire family. One of Edward III's most distinguished captains during the French wars, he fought at Sluys (1340) and Poitiers (1356). Subsequently a prominent courtier, politician and civil servant, he amassed a fortune and left detailed instructions for his elaborate tomb.

In 1822 the Dean and Chapter of Hereford Cathedral presented the helm to Sir Samuel Rush Meyrick, the first modern collector of armour. It was acquired in the 1870s by the Scottish painter, Sir Joseph Noel Paton, whose collection of arms and armour came to the Museum in 1905.

Gallery 2–14 *Arms and Armour*

Height 390 mm   A1905.289

43

Chilean rose

Tarantula moult from Chile

The spider, like other arthropods, has a hard outer covering, known as an exoskeleton, which supports and protects its body. This has to be shed at frequent intervals as the animal grows, in a process called moulting or ecdysis. The photograph shows the moult of a Chilean rose spider.

For some days before the moult the spider stops eating. It then rests on a mat of silk while a new exoskeleton forms in the space between the old one and the spider's shrunken body. Hormones called ecdysones control the whole moulting process. Fluid is produced below the old exoskeleton which then splits and the spider gently moves its body to widen the gap. Since the new exoskeleton is still quite soft the spider can manoeuvre itself out of the split, pulling its appendages, always in a set order, out of the old exoskeleton, rather as we pull our fingers out of a glove.

During the moult, the spider is able to regenerate a lost or damaged leg. The new leg will be smaller, but will grow to normal size after subsequent moults. Although the spider is weak, immobile and very vulnerable while moulting, its new exoskeleton hardens completely in one or two days.

Chilean spiders, with other large hairy spiders from the Americas, are commonly called tarantulas. As is well known, they kill their prey by poison, but they are shy creatures, not the voracious killers depicted in films and comic strips. Most of them are not fatal to humans. They live in forest clearings but in some areas are endangered by the pet trade.

Gallery 1-12   *Insects and Molluscs*

Length 80 mm

44

Teaching beetle

Papier-mâché model of a cockchafer, from France,
about 1900

The cockchafer (*Melolontha melolontha*) is a widely distributed insect often occurring in gardens. The larva feeds on roots, including those of crop plants, and the adult feeds on the leaves of trees. Full development takes four years. Adults are sometimes seen swarming around trees and bushes during early evening. Attracted into homes and porches by lights, they make their presence known by a loud humming.

This model cockchafer was bought by the University of Edinburgh as a teaching aid for its biology classes, at a time when comparative anatomy played a central role in all courses on zoology. It was made by a Parisian model maker who had a flourishing export trade at the turn of the century. Almost 300 millimetres (1 foot) in length, the model magnifies its prototype, the cockchafer beetle, fifteen times. The body opens up by unfastening two hooks on the underside. Each organ is labelled with a scientific name, in French, and is also numbered for further identification.

The beetle is made of papier-mâché, a favourite material in the nineteenth century. The technique, imported from the Far East, involved soaking paper in glue and pressing it into a mould. With various additives, detail can be rendered very precisely, as this model illustrates. The wings, which unfold to reveal each blood vessel and muscle, are made of rice paper.

The University of Edinburgh and the Museum were closely associated from the time when the University's natural history collections became part of the original Museum's foundation in 1855.

Gallery **1-12** *Insects and Molluscs*

Length 350 mm

– 45 –
Mates

Fibreglass cast of a dogfish

The lesser-spotted dogfish, *Scyliorhinus canicula,* inhabits the continental shelf waters of Europe and West Africa as far south as Senegal. This small shark, which grows to less than a metre in length, is used for food in many countries. In Britain it turns up on the fishmonger's slab as 'huss'; in the past the usual term was 'rock salmon'.

The sculptural form of this mating couple is scrupulously accurate, thanks to the Museum's award-winning taxidermists. With traditional methods of fish taxidermy, which preserve the skin, it is difficult to obtain lifelike positions, and the skins dry out and split. Modern displays, such as the Museum's gallery of fish biology, use casts made from actual fish arranged in the desired pose. The casts are realistically painted.

The male sharks have two 'claspers' – so-called because formerly it was thought that they grasped the female during mating. In fact these modified inner edges of the pelvic fins serve as a pair of penises (used one at a time). Sperm passes along the clasper into the female where it fertilizes her eggs. In the lesser-spotted dogfish fertilization does not necessarily occur immediately; the female can retain sperm for use several months later.

The eggs themselves are encased in a tough membrane which hardens as they are laid. At each corner of the egg case is a long tendril which helps to anchor it to the seabed. Sometimes the anchors give way and egg cases, popularly known as 'mermaids' purses', are washed up on beaches.

Gallery **1-7** *Fish caes 27*

Length 570 mm

46

Fish graveyard

Fossil fish from Dura Den, Fife, about
365 million years old

In the spring of 1836 workmen uncovered fish remains while digging a new mill-lade in Dura Den, a valley near Cupar, Fife. The local minister was alerted, who brought in scientists from the University of St Andrews. This particular slab, one of six, was collected by Professor Matthew Forster Heddle (1828-97), a distinguished geologist whose collection of rocks and minerals is now in the NMS.

The fish are entombed in a type of rock called the Old Red Sandstone which forms the coastal plains of eastern Scotland and in the 1830s was already known to have a distinctive fauna of freshwater fossils. The rock's actual age was not established until radioisotope dating was developed more than a century later. We now know that these fish lived about 365 million years ago, and that they became extinct about five million years later. They all belong to a group of fleshy-finned bony fish called Crossopterygii. It is generally thought that descendants of the Crossopterygii came ashore and ultimately gave rise to amphibians, which in turn evolved into reptiles, birds and mammals.

What led to so many fish dying in so small a pool? It was probably drought at the beginning of the dry season. Scotland was then much nearer the equator, with a seasonal climate like that of the Australian outback: severe drought alternating with rainy seasons. After the fish had dried and partly rotted, sand washed over them. The accumulated masses of sand sank and, by compaction and chemical change over millions of years, were converted into sandstone.

Gallery G-7 *Evolution Wing*

Width of slab 820 mm   G1966.39.14

47

Aldebran giant

Shell and skin of a giant tortoise from Aldebra Island

Many oceanic islands were once the habitat of giant tortoises, but now only two species survive: this one, *Geochelone gigantica*, native to the Indian Ocean island of Aldabra some 250 miles north of Madagascar, and its more famous cousin on the Galapagos. The giant tortoise is exclusively terrestrial, with the term 'turtle' usually applied to the aquatic or semi-aquatic varieties.

In the nineteenth century the Aldabran tortoise seemed on the verge of extinction, because the crews of passing ships killed them in huge numbers for fresh meat. In 1874 naturalists, including Charles Darwin, petitioned for a breeding population to be established on the Seychelles. This population survives in a *parc au tortue*, while on Aldabra itself numbers recovered are under protection. The island, now a UNESCO World Heritage Site, is said to teem with tortoises.

The tortoise is largely vegetarian although it will eat meat, mostly carrion, if it can get it. The female lays up to fourteen eggs and buries them in the sand. Once hatched, tortoises grow for 20 to 25 years, and can live as long as a century. Our representative is a male probably aged at least 30 years old. After his capture he lived for some years in London Zoo.

The males are larger than the females and have a concave lower shell (the plastron) which enables them to mount the female during mating. Ogden Nash nevertheless had a point when he wrote:

> The turtle lives twixt plated decks
> Which practic'ly conceal its sex.
> I think it clever of the turtle
> In such a fix to be so furtle.

Gallery   *G-10*   *Reptiles*

Length 1250 mm   Z1911.102

48

Misunderstood athlete

Model of a dodo, a species from Mauritius

'Fat, ungainly and awkward': for over three centuries the flightless dodo has been the victim of bad publicity.

Its only home was the island of Mauritius in the Indian Ocean. The island was uninhabited by man until the Portuguese arrived in 1507. They introduced pigs and monkeys which fed upon the young birds and the eggs. The Dutch, who arrived in 1598, and others after them, did further harm by destroying the dodo's forest habitat in their search for ebony. Within seventy years it was extinct.

Today, little trace of the species survives. There are some skeletons, put together from the thousands of bones found in a swamp on the island. A dried foot and head are in the Zoology Museum, Oxford; and another foot is in the British Museum. Modern museum models are based on seventeenth-century illustrations. Those from the early 1600s depict a fairly slim bird, but drawings after 1626, probably of dodos brought to Europe as curiosities, show them as sedentary and fat.

Recently, NMS research has shown that in its natural state, the dodo was slim and athletic. From the surviving bones, the dodo's weight has been estimated at about 14 kg (31lb) but in captivity, without exercise, it could expand to twice that. By calculating the relative strength of its leg bones, it was found that they were as strong as those of running birds such as ostriches – in other words, the dodo was a fast runner, something which was testified by the last eyewitness account in 1662.

The slim-line model is based on the results of this research.

Gallery **G-11** *World in Our Hands*

Height 650 mm   Z1993.048

49

Steam aristocrat

Model of the locomotive Waverley, *from Scotland, early 20th century*

The enormous *Waverley*, and twenty-one locomotives of similar design, were the aristocrats of their time. In 1906 the North British Railway met the challenge of rival railway companies by commissioning these new express passenger engines. The basic design was drawn up by William Paton Reid, the company's Locomotive Superintendent, and they were built at the North British Locomotive works in Glasgow.

The 4-4-2 arrangement of wheels – four wheels on the leading bogie, four coupled driving wheels and two trailing wheels – was first used in the eastern United States and known as 'Atlantic'. It was particularly suitable for the curving routes the locomotives were to service. They comfortably achieved almost 100 kilometres per hour (60mph) on the level. Because of their size, bridges and tracks on some routes had to be strengthened, and turntables lengthened.

For thirty years these locomotives hauled huge trains up formidable gradients, mostly on the Carlisle-Edinburgh-Aberdeen route and the Edinburgh-Perth route. At first, their crews were nervous of their power and the roll which developed through the large boilers being set rather high. But once established, they became the envy of crews on lesser engines.

For most of its working life the *Waverley* was based at Haymarket, Edinburgh. In 1923, when the North British Railway became part of the London and North Eastern Railway, it was painted in the green LNER livery and given an LNER number. The model was made soon after this by Mr Parr of Glasgow.

The *Waverley* was scrapped in 1937; the last Atlantic went for scrap in the war effort of 1939.

Gallery **G-21**

Length 1630 mm   T1927.43

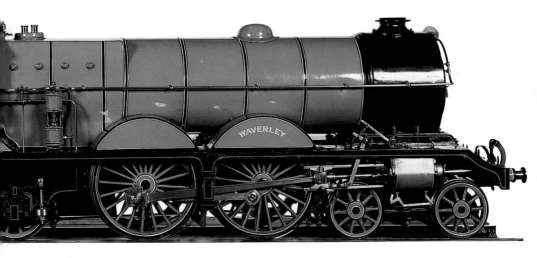

50

ALL-SCOTTISH

New Gerrard motorcycle from Scotland, 1924

The New Gerrard motorcycle was designed in 1922 by the renowned Scottish motorcycle racer Jock Porter, who named it after one of his sons. Until about 1939 it was built and sold in Porter's Motor Mart business at Greenside Place, Edinburgh.

The Museum's vehicle was made in 1924 and is probably the last surviving example of an all-Scottish bike. It is fitted with the Glasgow-built Barr and Stroud engine instead of the more common English-built Blackburne or JAP, and it predates the time when the frames were supplied by Campion in Nottingham.

The bike is a version of the New Gerrard intended for ordinary use. Other New Gerrard models were racing machines used by foreign riders and by Porter himself. Porter, the only international rider using bikes of his own design and manufacture, had many successes with the New Gerrard, including the 1923 Lightweight and 1924 Ultra-Lightweight events at the Isle of Man TT races, and ten Grand Prix wins in Europe. In the process he triumphed over New Imperial, Cotton and Rex-Acme works motorcycles.

Compared to the older Victoria motorcycle in the same display case, the New Gerrard's technical advances are the chain, as opposed to belt, drive and the all-alloy sleeve-valve engine. The exhaust system has evolved from a short cylindrical box to a sweeping pipe and stylish silencer while the almost straight handlebars allow the rider to crouch lower.

This bike spent most of its life on a Sma' Glen Farm in Perthshire where it was discovered about 25 years ago.

Gallery **G-21**

Length 2070 mm   T1990.18

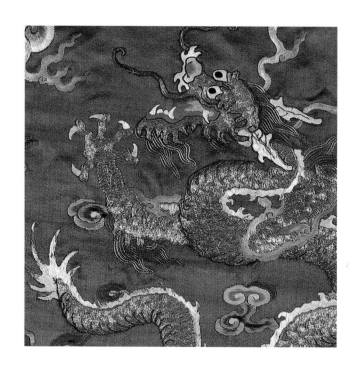

Booklist

Other publications from NMS

More information on Royal Museum of Scotland collections can be found in the following publications from the NMS:

R G W Anderson (ed) *The Playfair Collection* pbk £10.00
W J Baird *The Scenery of Scotland. The Structure Beneath* pbk £3.99
I Bunyan et al *No Ordinary Journey. John Rae, Arctic Explorer 1813-1893* pbk £4.99
C Curnow *Italian Maiolica in the National Museums of Scotland* pbk £35.00
S Irvine *Bird Facts* (co-published with HMSO) pbk £4.50
A Kitchener *Escape from Extinction* (co-published with HMSO) pbk £4.50
E Kwasnik (ed) *A Wider World* pbk £17.95
H Macpherson *Agates* pbk £5.95
J Scarce *Domestic Culture in the Middle East* (co-published with Curzon Press) pbk £12.99
A D C Simpson (ed) *Joseph Black 1728-1799* pbk £10.00
G Swinney *Fish Facts* (co-published with HMSO) pbk £3.95
N Tarrant *The Development of Costume* (co-published with Routledge) hbk £35.00 pbk £11.99
J Wilkinson and N Pearce *Harmony and Contrast. A Journey through East Asian Art* (co-published with Curzon Press) pbk £12.99

Books on Scottish material, relating to the Museum of Scotland due to open in 1998, include:

C Brown *Feeding Scotland* pbk £4.99
J Burnett *Sporting Scotland* pbk £4.99
J Calder *The Enterprising Scot* pbk £3.99
J Calder *Treasure Islands. A Robert Louis Stevenson Anthology* pbk £6.95
J Calder (ed) *The Wealth of a Nation* hbk £8.99 pbk £5.99
A Carruthers (ed) *The Scottish Home* hbk £25.00

H Cheape *Tartan* pbk £5.99

G Dalgleish and D Mechan *'I am Come Home'. Treasures of Prince Charles Edward Stuart* pbk £1.75

A Dodds *Making Cars* pbk £4.99

E Gauldie *Spinning and Weaving* pbk £4.99

J Graham-Campbell *The Viking-Age Gold and Silver of Scotland* AD 850-1100 hbk £55.00

D Kidd *To See Oursels. Rural Scotland in Old Photographs* hbk £15.99

L Leneman *Into the Foreground. Scottish Women in Photographs* hbk £15.99

I McGregor *Bairns. Scottish Children in Photographs* hbk £14.99 pbk £9.99

M McLeod *Leaving Scotland* pbk £4.99

A Martin *Fishing and Whaling* pbk £4.99

A Martin *Scottish Endings. An Illustrated Anthology of Death* pbk £7.99

A Martin *Scotland's Weather. An Illustrated Anthology* pbk £6.99

R M Spearman and J Higgitt *The Age of Migrating Ideas. Early Medieval Art in Northern Britain and Ireland* co-published with Sutton Publishing pbk £35.00

G Sprott *Farming* pbk £4.99

G Sprott *Robert Burns, Farmer* pbk £1.99

J Wood *Building Railways* pbk £4.99

CD-ROM *Investigating the Lewis Chess Pieces/ Sùil air Fir-Tàileisg Leòdhais* £13.99

All these books are available in the Museum Shop at the Royal Museum of Scotland, Chambers Street, Edinburgh. Books published by NMS alone can be obtained by post from NMS Publishing, National Museums of Scotland, Chambers Street, Edinburgh EH1 1JF. Please add 15% of total value (minimum £1) for postage and packing. Co-published books can be obtained from the co-publisher.